WHERE'S THE SPOOKY POO?

ORCHARD

ORCHARD BOOKS

First published in Great Britain in 2020
by The Watts Publishing Group

3 5 7 9 10 8 6 4 2

© 2020 The Watts Publishing Group Limited

Illustrations by Dynamo Limited

Additional images © Shutterstock

A CIP catalogue record for this book is available from the British Library

ISBN 978 1 40836 310 2

Printed and bound in China

FSC
www.fsc.org
MIX
Paper from
responsible sources
FSC® C104740

Orchard Books
An imprint of Hachette Children's Group
Part of The Watts Publishing Group Limited
Carmelite House
50 Victoria Embankment
London EC4Y 0DZ

An Hachette UK Company
www.hachette.co.uk
www.hachettechildrens.co.uk

WHERE'S THE
SPOOKY
POO?

THE SCARIEST POOS IN THE WORLD

The spooky poos love being scary, especially on Halloween, their favourite night of the year.

Can you spot each of the poos in every scene?

Look out for Jack the Pumpkin Poo hiding in one of the scenes, too!

HOWL

the Werewolf Poo turns into a scary, hairy monster whenever there's a full moon.

DRAC

the Vampire Poo loves sleeping all day. Then he nips out at night for a tasty snack – but hold the garlic!

BOO

the Ghost Poo has been haunting people since the day she was flushed away.

LOU

the Mummy Poo has been preserved for years wrapped in toilet paper! As the oldest and wisest poo in the gang, she's in charge.

FRANKIE

the Monster Poo is the biggest and strongest of the gang. But don't be too scared, he's a real softy on the inside!

PUMPKIN PATCH

Boo's favourite food is pumpkin pie so she's taken the gang pumpkin-picking. Can you spot them down on the farm?

PUMPKIN PATCH

POOPERMARKET

The spooky poos are stocking up on sweets for trick-or-treating! Can you see the fearsome friends?

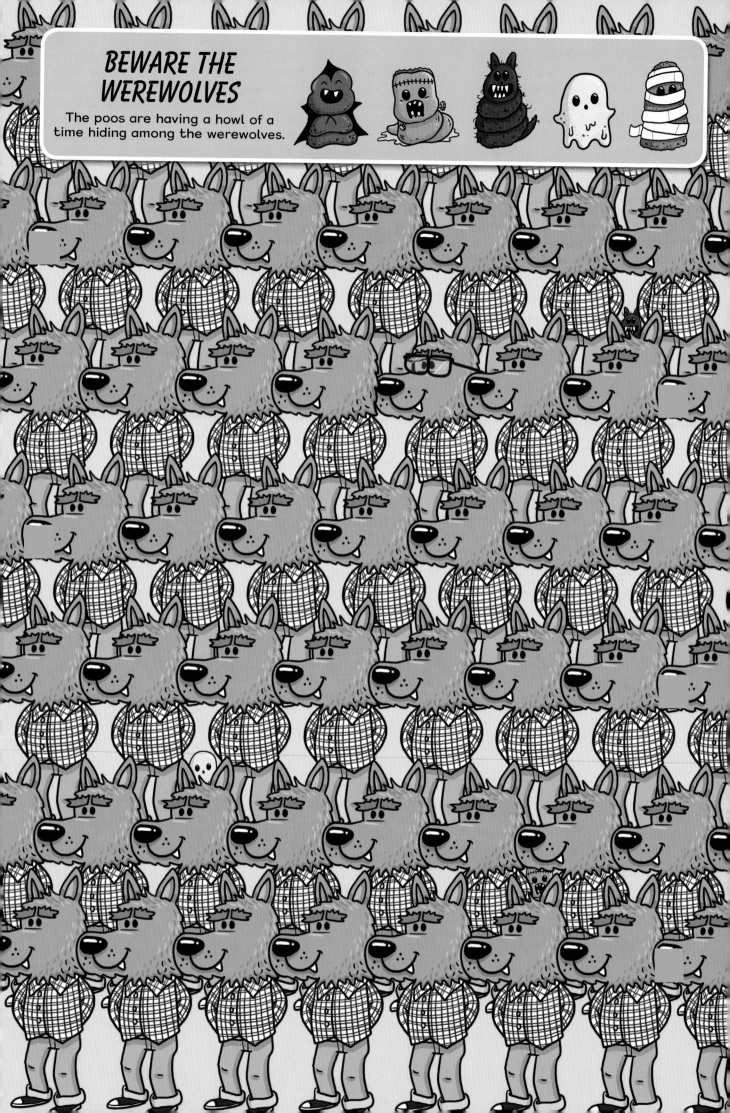

BEWARE THE WEREWOLVES

The poos are having a howl of a time hiding among the werewolves.

FRIGHT NIGHT DISCO

The spooky poos love to boogie! Can you see them all breaking out their dance moves?

FRIGHTENING FAST FOOD

All this running around has made the poos a little peckish. Can you spot them grabbing a bite to eat?

SPIDER TERROR

He might look super scary, but Frankie is secretly terrified of spiders! Can you find him and all his friends?

ODD ONE OUT!

Which spider is different from the others?

GHOST TRAIN

Boo has invited all her spooky poo friends for a day at the theme park. The ghost train is her favourite ride, what's yours?

TRICK-OR-TREAT

Howl loves seeing everyone's trick-or-treating costumes. What do you like to dress up as for Halloween?

VAMPIRE PARTY

All the poos like to party, especially Drac – he loves dancing all night long!

ODD ONE OUT!

Which of the vampires is the odd one out?

POO PARADE

It's hard to tell who's in costume at the parade. Can you spot Frankie and his friends as they join in?

SPOOKS POO-NITED

With the spooky poos haunting the match, fans may see more ghouls than goals!

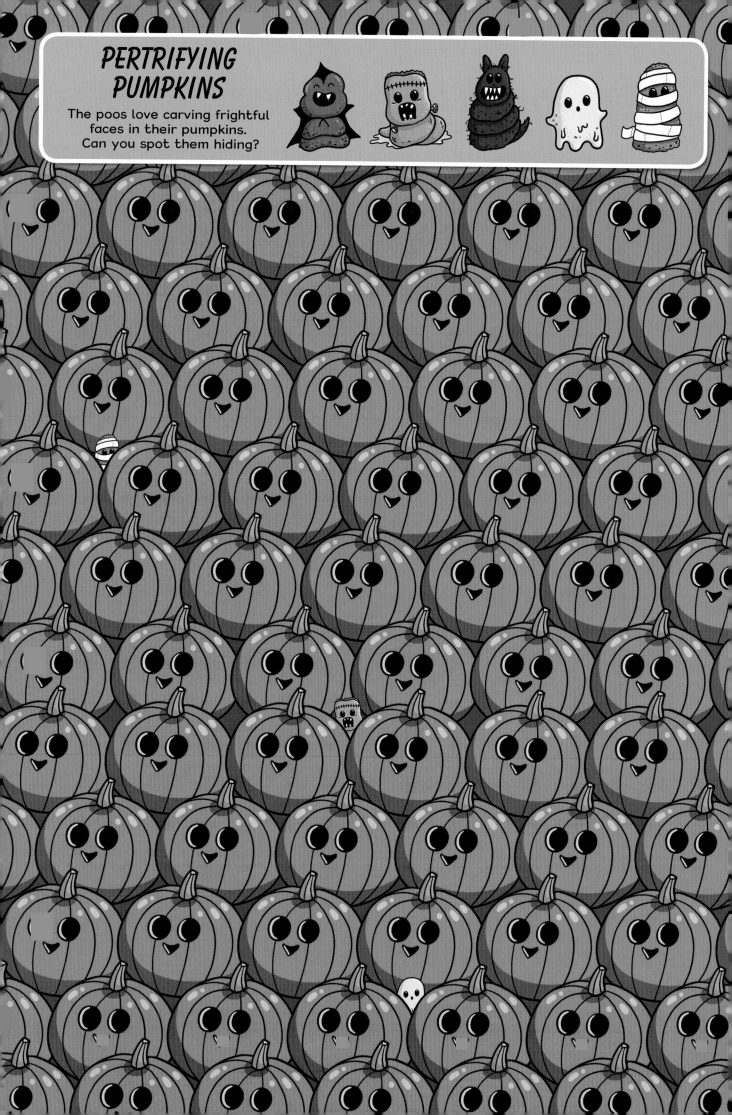

PERTRIFYING PUMPKINS

The poos love carving frightful faces in their pumpkins. Can you spot them hiding?

ODD ONE OUT!

One of the pumpkins is different from the rest. Can you find it?

HAUNTED HOUSE

Boo has brought her friends to one of her favourite haunts. Can you find them all exploring?

MONSTERS IN THE MUSEUM

Lou is enjoying meeting her Mummy friends in the museum. Find the friends having a spooktacular time.

ANSWERS

Now try and find the extra items hidden in each scene.

PUMPKIN PATCH

Ten hay bales	☐
Six cats	☐
A boy holding a teddy	☐
Fifteen blackbirds	☐
A weather vane	☐
A curious bear	☐
A person blowing their nose	☐
A yellow satchel	☐
Three scarecrows	☐
Six signposts	☐

POOPERMARKET

Seven pointy hats	☐
Four ghosts	☐
Ten cobwebs	☐
Thirteen spiders	☐
Eleven trollies	☐
Seven dinosaurs	☐
A pineapple	☐
Three bats	☐
A broomstick	☐
Two mummies	☐

BEWARE THE WEREWOLVES

FRIGHT NIGHT DISCO

Three cobwebs ☐

Five green balloons ☐

Four disco balls ☐

Fifteen pointy hats ☐

Six people wearing horns ☐

Eight ghosts ☐

Two werewolves ☐

Four skull masks ☐

A person in a bunny costume ☐

A smiley face mask ☐

FRIGHTENING FAST FOOD

Six carved pumpkins ☐

Five ghosts ☐

Twenty-three burgers ☐

Nine spiders ☐

Six salads ☐

Thirteen milkshakes ☐

Twenty-one bottles of ketchup ☐

Nineteen menus ☐

Nine cobwebs ☐

Seven rollerskaters ☐

SPIDER TERROR

GHOST TRAIN

Five spiders	☐
Three costumes with wings	☐
Four mummies	☐
Six ghosts	☐
Twelve pointy hats	☐
A clown	☐
Six birds	☐
Three hotdogs	☐
Twenty-two trees	☐
A pumpkin costume	☐

TRICK-OR-TREAT

Sixteen pumpkins	☐
Eight spiders	☐
Eight bats	☐
Fourteen birds	☐
Five ghosts	☐
Five dogs	☐
Nine skulls	☐
A teddy bear	☐
Two snakes	☐
Twelve people with moustaches	☐

VAMPIRE PARTY

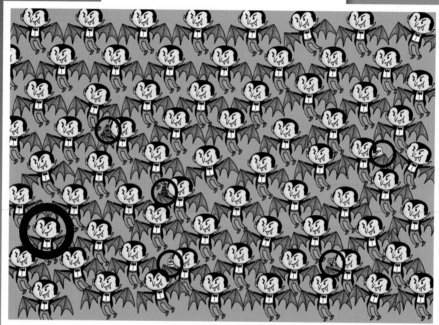

POO PARADE

- Three rainbow umbrellas ☐
- Eighteen lanterns ☐
- A unicyclist ☐
- Five poeple playing marraccas ☐
- An ice cream ☐
- A loudhaler ☐
- Seventeen floral headbands ☐
- Three butterfly costumes ☐
- Thirty-one hats ☐
- A purple flag ☐

SPOOKS POO-NITED

Fifteen boxes of popcorn ☐

Fifteen foam fingers ☐

Seven pies ☐

Eight ghosts ☐

Twenty-two hot dogs ☐

Two number 13s ☐

Seven werewolves ☐

Four pointy hats ☐

Five vampires playing football ☐

Thirty-two cups ☐

PETRIFYING PUMPKINS

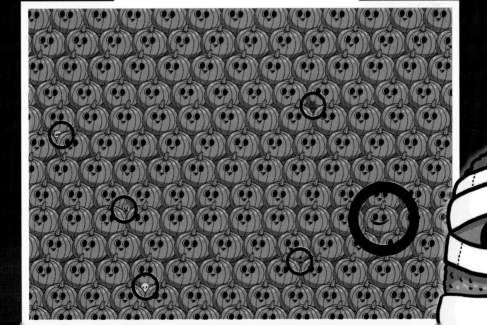

Did you find me? If you're stuck, try visiting the museum again.

HAUNTED HOUSE

- Twenty-three bats ☐
- A monster brushing his teeth ☐
- Two broomsticks ☐
- Twenty-four pumpkins ☐
- A mummy drinking a cup of tea ☐
- Nine green hands with no bodies ☐
- A bird wearing a witch's hat ☐
- Three cats ☐
- A jar of eyeballs ☐
- Two birds eating chips ☐

SCARY SLEEPOVER

- Eight snakes ☐
- Three people drawing ☐
- Four mice ☐
- Three mummified dogs ☐
- Ten beetles ☐
- A falling vase ☐
- Five people wearing headphones ☐
- Five pillars ☐
- Six clipboards ☐
- A mouse hole ☐